Specific Skill Series

Working Within Words

Richard A. Boning

Fifth Edition

SRA/McGraw-Hill

Columbus, Ohio

Cover, Back Cover, Ron Sanford/The Stock Market

SRA/McGraw-Hill

A Division of The **McGraw·Hill** *Companies*

Printed in the United States of America.

Send all inquiries to:
    SRA/McGraw-Hill
    250 Old Wilson Bridge Road, Suite 310
    Worthington, OH 43085

ISBN 0-02-687926-3

    3 4 5 6 7 8 9 IMP 00 99 98

To the Teacher

PURPOSE:
WORKING WITHIN WORDS helps pupils put sounds and other word elements to work to determine word meaning. Many units in WORKING WITHIN WORDS develop understandings about sound-symbol (phonic) associations. Other units treat letter combinations, syllabication, roots and affixes, accent patterns, compound words, longer words, and spelling changes caused by adding endings.

FOR WHOM:
The skill of WORKING WITHIN WORDS is developed through a series of books spanning ten levels (Picture, Preparatory, A, B, C, D, E, F, G, H). The Picture Level is for pupils who have not acquired a basic sight vocabulary. The Preparatory Level is for pupils who have a basic sight vocabulary but are not yet ready for the first-grade-level book. Books A through H are appropriate for pupils who can read on levels one through eight, respectively. **The use of the *Specific Skill Series Placement Test* is recommended to determine the appropriate level.**

THE NEW EDITION:
The fifth edition of the *Specific Skill Series* maintains the quality and focus that has distinguished this program for more than 25 years. A key element central to the program's success has been the unique nature of the reading selections. Nonfiction pieces about current topics have been designed to stimulate the interest of students, motivating them to use the comprehension strategies they have learned to further their reading. To keep this important aspect of the program intact, a percentage of the reading selections have been replaced in order to ensure the continued relevance of the subject material.

In addition, a significant percentage of the artwork in the program has been replaced to give the books a contemporary look. The cover photographs are designed to appeal to readers of all ages.

SESSIONS:
Short practice sessions are the most effective. It is desirable to have a practice session every day or every other day, using a few units each session.

SCORING:
Pupils should record their answers on the reproducible worksheets. The worksheets make scoring easier and provide uniform records of the pupils' work. Using worksheets also avoids consuming the exercise books.

It is important for pupils to know how well they are doing. For this reason, units should be scored as soon as they have been completed. Then a discussion can be held in which pupils justify their choices. (The Integrated Language Activities, many of which are open-ended, do not lend themselves to an objective score; thus there are no answer keys for these pages.)

GENERAL INFORMATION ON *WORKING WITHIN WORDS*:

The units are of two types: concept builders and functional exercises. The concept units focus the reader's attention on common patterns and parts of words. Each generalization is built step-by-step on the structure of previously formed concepts. The functional exercises either follow the concept units or are contained within them. They provide the reader with many immediate and repeated experiences with words involving particular patterns or principles. Sentence settings are typical for the pupils' level; often the choices offered are new words.

As WORKING WITHIN WORDS progresses through different word elements there is constant reinforcement. The more elementary booklets focus on phonic elements such as consonant sounds, consonant substitutions, blends, phonograms, and vowel sounds. As the level of difficulty increases, the emphasis shifts to syllabication, prefixes, suffixes, and roots.

A unit-by-unit list of concepts developed in this book is found on page 64.

INSTRUCTIONS:

Minimal direction is required. Pupils' attention must be drawn to the answer choices. In the concept units only two or three answer choices are offered. In the units that provide application of understandings, four to nine answer choices are offered, providing more experiences with words of a particular pattern. In units which offer an *F* choice, the *F* stands for NONE. This means that none of the choices makes sense in that particular setting.

RELATED MATERIALS:

Specific Skill Series Placement Tests, which enable the teacher to place pupils at their appropriate levels in each skill, are available for the Elementary (Pre-1–6) and Midway (4–8) grade levels.

About This Book

In written words, letters stand for sounds. A reader **decodes** a word the way a spy decodes a secret message. If you know the sounds that letters stand for, you can begin to unlock the secret message of a word.

Knowing the sounds of a word is only a beginning. Just as a secret message may have many parts, a word may have more than one part, too. In order to read and understand a word, you need to understand the parts of the word.

Sometimes two words are joined together to make a *compound* word. What two words are joined to make the word *heartbeat*? What does *heartbeat* mean?

Word parts can be added to words to make new words with new meanings. For example, you may have ridden a *tricycle* when you were little but a *bicycle* when you were bigger. How did the word parts *tri* and *bi* affect the meanings?

Some words are related to each other in both meaning and spelling because they have a common *root*. A *root* is often not a word by itself, but it is part of many different words. The root *vis*, for example, comes from a Latin word that means "to see." These words are all formed from one common root: *vision, visual, invisible*. How are their meanings related?

In this book, you will study many words. You will learn to recognize the parts of words and patterns in words. Then you will use what you have learned. As you unlock the meanings of the words in this book, you will be practicing the skills of a master decoder!

UNIT 1
Prefix Concepts and Practice—ad, ob, op

1. The prefix **ad** means **to** or **toward. Advance,** for example, means **to go forward. Advertise** means **to turn people's attention** _____ **a product.**
   (A) against   (B) to

2. The word that means **sticking to something** is _____.
   (A) adhesive   (B) adapt   (C) adequate

3. The word that means **to manage or direct** is _____.
   (A) advent   (B) administer   (C) advance

4. The word that means **to allow to enter** is _____.
   (A) adverb   (B) adopt   (C) admit

5. From the examples we have just studied we can tell that the prefix _____ means **to** or **toward.**
   (A) un   (B) ad   (C) re

6. The prefixes **op/ob** mean **toward, to, against,** or **over. Obverse,** for example, means **turned toward** or **facing. Oppose** means **to go** _____.
   (A) backward   (B) against

7. The word that means **that which stands in the way** is _____.
   (A) obstacle   (B) oppose   (C) objection

8. The word that means **unjust use of power** is _____.
   (A) object   (B) oppression   (C) obstruction

9. The word that means **to give a reason against** is _____.
   (A) object   (B) oblique   (C) obnoxious

10. From the examples we have just studied we can tell that the prefix _____ means **toward, to, against,** or **over.**
    (A) ob   (B) un   (C) re

1. The prefix **ir** means **not. Irresponsible,** for example, means **not responsible. Irresistible** means _____ resistible.

   (A) **not**   (B) **sometimes**

2. The word that means **not making sense is** _____.

   (A) **irrecoverable**   (B) **irrational**   (C) **irrepressible**

3. The word that means **cannot be made smaller is** _____.

   (A) **irreligious**   (B) **irrefutable**   (C) **irreducible**

4. The word that means **not regular** is _____.

   (A) **irregular**   (B) **irreversible**   (C) **irreplaceable**

5. From the examples we have studied we can tell that the prefix _____ means **not.**

   (A) **de**   (B) **be**   (C) **ir**

6. The prefix **il** means **not. Illegal,** for example, means **not allowed by the law. Illiterate** means _____ **able to read or write.**

   (A) **always**   (B) **not**

7. The word that means **not read easily because badly written or printed** is _____.

   (A) **illiberal**   (B) **illegible**   (C) **illogical**

8. The word that means **endless** or **having no limit** is _____.

   (A) **ill-mannered**   (B) **illiberal**   (C) **illimitable**

9. The word that means **not logical** or **showing poor reasoning** is _____.

   (A) **illegible**   (B) **illogical**   (C) **ill-natured**

10. From the examples we have just studied we can tell that the prefix _____ means **not.**

    (A) **re**   (B) **il**   (C) **uni**

1. The element **uni** or **uno** means **one,** or **having one,** or **made of one. Unit** means **any group of things considered as one. Unicycle** means **a vehicle that has** _____.
    (A) **a single wheel**   (B) **two wheels**

2. The word that means **regular** or **not changing** is _____.
    (A) **universe**   (B) **uniform**   (C) **union**

3. The word that means **oneness** or **being united** is _____.
    (A) **unicellular**   (B) **unity**   (C) **unipolar**

4. The word that means **having only one side** is _____.
    (A) **unicorn**   (B) **unitary**   (C) **unilateral**

5. From the examples we have just studied we can tell that the prefix _____ means **one, having one,** or **made of one.**
    (A) **uni**   (B) **tri**   (C) **bi**

6. The element **mono** means _____. **Monocular,** for example, means **one-eyed. Monodrama** means **a drama written for a single actor.**
    (A) **one**   (B) **two**

7. The word that means **railway having cars that run on a single rail** is _____.
    (A) **monograph**   (B) **monorail**   (C) **monoculture**

8. The word that means **a one-wheeled vehicle** is _____.
    (A) **monoplane**   (B) **monochrome**   (C) **monocycle**

9. The word that means **having one sound** is _____.
    (A) **monotone**   (B) **monocle**   (C) **monogamy**

10. From the examples we have just studied we can tell that the element _____ means **one.**
    (A) **ab**   (B) **dis**   (C) **mono**

1. The prefix **bi** means **twice** or **two. Biweekly,** for example, means **twice a week. Bifocal** means having _____ focuses.
   (A) two   (B) three

2. The word that means **twice a year** is _____.
   (A) biannual   (B) binoculars   (C) biparty

3. The word that means **to divide into two equal parts** is _____.
   (A) bisect   (B) bicycle   (C) biped

4. The word that means **able to speak two languages** is _____.
   (A) bilingual   (B) bipolar   (C) bilateral

5. From the examples we have just studied we can tell that the prefix _____ means **twice** or **two.**
   (A) bi   (B) tri   (C) uni

6. The prefix **tri** means **three, three times, having three parts,** or **every third. Triplicate** means **three copies. Triangle** means **a figure having three angles. Trimonthly** means **every** _____ month.
   (A) second   (B) third

7. The word that means a **three-wheeled vehicle** is _____.
   (A) trio   (B) tricycle   (C) triple

8. The word that means **having three colors** is _____.
   (A) trident   (B) tricolor   (C) triplane

9. The word that means **any three people or things joined or associated** is _____.
   (A) trio   (B) tricuspid   (C) trilateral

10. From the examples we have just studied we can see that the prefix _____ means **three, three times, having three parts,** or **every third.**
    (A) tri   (B) bi   (C) de

1. The element **cent** means **one hundred** or **one hundredth of**. A **centavo**, for example, means **a small coin equal to one hundredth of the monetary unit**. **Centigrade** means **graduated to a scale of one** _____.
   (A) **hundred**   (B) **thousand**

2. The word that means **a tiny animal with one hundred legs** is _____.
   (A) **centipede**   (B) **centenary**   (C) **centesimal**

3. The word that means **one who is 100 years old** is _____.
   (A) **centimeter**   (B) **centenarian**   (C) **century**

4. The word that means **100th anniversary** is _____.
   (A) **centuplicate**   (B) **centennial**   (C) **centigram**

5. From the examples we have just studied we can tell that the element _____ means **one hundred** or **one hundredth of**.
   (A) **uni**   (B) **cent**   (C) **tri**

6. The prefix **semi** means **partly, half,** or **twice**. A **semiprecious** stone is somewhat valuable. A **semitropical** zone is halfway between temperate and tropical. A **semiweekly** paper is issued _____ a week.
   (A) **once**   (B) **twice**

7. The word that means **almost finished** is _____.
   (A) **semitone**   (B) **semiprofessional**   (C) **semicomplete**

8. The word that means **taking place about every fifteen days** is _____.
   (A) **semimonthly**   (B) **semiweekly**   (C) **semiperfect**

9. The word that means **partly without water** is _____.
   (A) **semifinal**   (B) **semipublic**   (C) **semiarid**

10. From the examples we have just studied we can tell that the prefix _____ means **partly, half,** or **twice.**
    (A) **ultra**   (B) **pre**   (C) **semi**

1. The prefix **kilo** means **one thousand.** A **kilowatt,** for example, is a unit of electrical power equal to **1,000 watts.** A **kilometer** is a unit of distance in the metric system equal to _____ meters.

   (A) 100   (B) 1,000

2. The word that means **a unit of weight equal to 1,000 grams** is _____.

   (A) kilogram   (B) kilovolt   (C) kilocalorie

3. The word that means **a unit used to measure the frequency of radio waves equal to 1,000 cycles** is _____.

   (A) kilobar   (B) kilocycle   (C) kiloliter

4. The word that means **a unit of capacity in the metric system equal to 1,000 liters** is _____.

   (A) kiloton   (B) kilovolt   (C) kiloliter

5. From the examples we have just studied we can tell that the prefix _____ means **one thousand.**

   (A) centi   (B) kilo   (C) semi

6. The prefix **milli** means **one thousandth of.** A **milligram** means **one thousandth of a gram. Milliliter,** for example, means _____ a liter.

   (A) one thousandth of   (B) one tenth of

7. The word that means **one thousandth of a second** is _____.

   (A) milliwatt   (B) milligal   (C) millisecond

8. The word that means **one thousandth of a volt of electricity** is _____.

   (A) milligram   (B) millivolt   (C) millidegree

9. The word that means **a unit of barometric pressure equal to one thousandth of a bar** is _____.

   (A) millibar   (B) millimeter   (C) milligram

10. From the examples we have just studied we can tell that the prefix _____ means **one thousandth of.**

    (A) semi   (B) milli   (C) bi

1. The prefix **re** means **again** or **once more. Reread,** for example, means **to read again. Reappear** means **to appear** _____.
   (A) **again**   (B) **quickly**

2. The word that means **to put in order again** is _____.
   (A) **refill**   (B) **rearrange**   (C) **reheat**

3. The word that means **to restore confidence** is _____.
   (A) **reassure**   (B) **reopen**   (C) **reconquer**

4. The word that means **to construct again** is _____.
   (A) **rebuild**   (B) **reappear**   (C) **recur**

5. From the examples we have just studied we can tell that the prefix _____ means **again** or **once more.**
   (A) **sub**   (B) **re**   (C) **inter**

6. The prefix **pro** means **forward, forth, in favor of. Propel** means **to drive forward. Pro-American** means _____ **America.**
   (A) **in favor of**   (B) **against**

7. The word that means **to bring forth or into existence** is _____.
   (A) **project**   (B) **produce**   (C) **profess**

8. The word that means **to jut forward** is _____.
   (A) **prospect**   (B) **protrude**   (C) **program**

9. The word that means **to advance in grade or importance** is _____.
   (A) **promote**   (B) **profess**   (C) **produce**

10. From the examples we have just studied we can tell that the prefix _____ means **forward, forth,** or **in favor of.**
    (A) **bene**   (B) **mal**   (C) **pro**

1. The prefix **anti** means **against, opposed to,** or **the opposite of. Anti-aircraft,** for example, means **against aircraft. Anti-social** means _____ social.

    (A) the opposite of   **(B) in favor of**

2. The word that means **a substance that prevents growth of germs** is

    _____ .

    (A) antiseptic   **(B) antismoking**   **(C) antisocial**

3. The word that means **a liquid that prevents freezing** is _____ .

    (A) antifreeze   **(B) antifriction**   **(C) antiparticle**

4. The word that means **a medicine that works against the harmful effects of a poison or unwanted condition** is _____ .

    (A) antidote   **(B) antithesis**   **(C) antihuman**

5. From the examples we have just studied we can tell that the prefix _____ means **against** or **opposed to.**

    (A) anti   **(B) sub**   **(C) pre**

6. The prefix **contra** means **against** or **the opposite. Contrary,** for example, means **inclined to** _____ or **go against. Contralateral** means **on an opposite side.**

    (A) like   **(B) oppose**

7. The word that means **an opposite position** is _____ .

    (A) contraposition   **(B) contrary**   **(C) contravene**

8. The word that means **goods imported or exported against the law** is

    _____ .

    (A) contrast   **(B) contraband**   **(C) contradictory**

9. The word that means **to speak against another's statement** is _____ .

    (A) contravene   **(B) controversy**   **(C) contradict**

10. From the examples we have just studied we can tell that the prefix _____ means **against** or **the opposite.**

    (A) contra   **(B) pro**   **(C) pre**

1. The prefix **ab** means **away, from,** or **off. Absent,** for example, means _____ or **not present. Absolve** means **to declare free from blame or guilt.**
    (A) away   (B) not away

2. The word that means **to carry away** is _____.
    (A) **abduct**   (B) **abstract**   (C) **abscess**

3. The word that means **breaking off suddenly** is _____.
    (A) **abrupt**   (B) **absorb**   (C) **abstain**

4. The word that means **to do away with something** is _____.
    (A) **absentee**   (B) **abolish**   (C) **abroad**

5. From the examples we have just studied we can tell that the prefix _____ means **away, from,** or **off.**
    (A) **mis**   (B) **ab**   (C) **com**

6. The prefix **de** means **down, from, off,** or **the opposite of. Demolish,** for example, means **to pull down** or **destroy. Dethrone** means to _____ **the throne. Decamp** means **to go away from** or **leave camp.**
    (A) **force down from**   (B) **put on**

7. The word that means **to go down** is _____.
    (A) **descend**   (B) **deflect**   (C) **detach**

8. The word that means **to spread or distribute authority** is _____.
    (A) **decentralize**   (B) **describe**   (C) **define**

9. The word that means **to go ashore from a vessel** is _____.
    (A) **debark**   (B) **determine**   (C) **depend**

10. From the examples we have just studied we can tell that the prefix _____ means **down, away from, off,** or **the opposite of.**
    (A) **un**   (B) **de**   (C) **mal**

UNIT 10
Prefix Concepts and Practice—un, dis

1. The prefix **un** sometimes means **the opposite of. Unsafe,** for example, means **the opposite of safe. Un** also means **not.** The word _____, for example, means **not successful.**
    (A) unsuccessful   (B) success

2. The word that means **the opposite of put a disguise on** is _____.
    (A) unmask   (B) unseal   (C) unwrap

3. The word that means **not common** is _____.
    (A) unusual   (B) unhappy   (C) unfortunate

4. The word that means **not knowing** is _____.
    (A) unlucky   (B) untidy   (C) unwitting

5. From the examples we have just studied we can tell that the prefix _____ means **the opposite of** or **not.**
    (A) ex   (B) re   (C) un

6. The prefix **dis** sometimes means **the opposite of. Disappear,** for example, means **the opposite of come into sight. Dis** also means **not.** The word _____, for example, means **not polite.**
    (A) discourteous   (B) courteous

7. The word that means **the opposite of join together** is _____.
    (A) disunite   (B) disrepute   (C) dishonesty

8. The word that means **not faithful** is _____.
    (A) distasteful   (B) dismantle   (C) disloyal

9. The word that means **the opposite of good condition** is _____.
    (A) distinguish   (B) disrepair   (C) display

10. From the examples we have just studied we can tell that the prefix _____ means **the opposite of** or **not.**
    (A) re   (B) dis   (C) ab

15

1. Some prefixes have more than one meaning. The prefix **over** can mean **too much,** or **beyond the normal or desired point. Overbuild,** for example, means **to build** _____ **or too elaborately.**
   (A) **too much**   (B) **some**

2. The word that means **beyond the regular hours** is _____.
   (A) **overblow**   (B) **overtime**   (C) **overload**

3. The prefix **over** can also mean **higher in rank** or **superior. Overlord,** for example, means **a person who is lord** _____ **another lord or other lords.**
   (A) **over**   (B) **under**   (C) **with**

4. The word that means **a person who watches over others or their work** is _____.
   (A) **overlooker**   (B) **overlordship**   (C) **overseer**

5. The prefix **over** can also mean **covered** or **worn as an outer covering. Overcoat,** for example, means **an outer coat** or _____.
   (A) **warm**   (B) **covering**   (C) **thought**

6. The word that means **loose trousers worn over clothes to keep them clean** is _____.
   (A) **overalls**   (B) **overblouse**   (C) **overcast**

7. The prefix **over** can also mean **across** or **above. Overhead,** for example, means **far** _____ or **over the head.**
   (A) **above**   (B) **in**   (C) **away**

8. The word that means **across the ocean** is _____.
   (A) **overseas**   (B) **overhand**   (C) **overarm**

9. The prefix **over** has several meanings. From these examples, we can tell that the prefix **over** can mean _____ or **beyond the normal or desired point. Over** can mean **higher in rank** or **superior.**
   (A) **too little**   (B) **always**   (C) **too much**

10. The examples in this unit also show us that **over** can mean _____ or **worn as an outer covering.** In addition, **over** can mean **above** or **superior.**
    (A) **free**   (B) **covered**   (C) **through**

UNIT 12
Prefix Concepts and Practice—sub

1. Some prefixes have more than one meaning. The prefix **sub** can mean **under, below,** or **lower in rank, position, or importance. Submarine,** for example, means **a boat that can operate** _____ **water.**
   (A) under   (B) without

2. The word that means **a secondary heading or title** is _____.
   (A) subway   (B) substandard   (C) subhead

3. The word that means **a bringing under some power or influence** is _____.
   (A) subjection   (B) suborder   (C) subchief

4. The word that means **to put under water** is _____.
   (A) subject   (B) submerge   (C) submit

5. From these examples, we can tell that the prefix _____ can mean **under, below,** or **lower in rank, position, or importance.**
   (A) super   (B) sub   (C) syn

6. The prefix **sub** can also mean **nearly, somewhat, slightly, again,** or **further. Subarctic,** for example, means _____ **the Arctic region.**
   (A) near   (B) over   (C) above

7. The word that means **to divide again** is _____.
   (A) subaquatic   (B) subhumid   (C) subdivide

8. The word that means **not wholly conscious** is _____.
   (A) subconscious   (B) subarid   (C) subclassify

9. The word that means **a partly fossilized animal or plant** is _____.
   (A) sublease   (B) subfossil   (C) subculture

10. From these examples, we can tell that the prefix _____ can also mean **nearly, somewhat, again,** or **further.**
    (A) sym   (B) sub   (C) syl

17

Prefixes are word parts that are added at the beginning of a root word. Prefixes have meaning, but only when they are attached to root words. They cannot be used as words by themselves. The prefix *cent*, for instance, means "one hundred" or "one hundredth of." A *centipede* is an insect with one hundred legs.

A. Exercising Your Skill

The best way to travel is usually by taking the quickest and easiest route. The same is true for speech. If you have something to say, in most cases you should get to the point as quickly as possible. Prefixes help to make speech clear and brief. Look at the word *centipede*. Thanks to the prefix *cent*, these five words—animal with one hundred legs—are reduced to one.

Look at the prefixes below. What do they have in common? That's right—they all have something to do with numbers. Now look at the words in the box. On your paper, combine the words in the box with one or more of the prefixes. Then think of other words that contain these prefixes. Add them to your lists. Look up each word in a dictionary to check its spelling.

bi	cent(i)	kilo	uni
____	____	____	____
____	____	____	____
____	____	____	____

weekly	form	liter
corn	grade	meter
cycle	gram	yearly

B. Expanding Your Skill

Even though prefixes are not words, you can find their meanings in the dictionary. Look up the meanings of *bi*, *kilo*, *cent* (or *centi*) and *uni*. Then look up the meanings of all the words you listed. Notice how the meaning of each whole word is related to the meaning of its prefix.

When you are done, use the dictionary to find other words that begin with these prefixes. Write these new words on your paper.

C. Exploring Language

You have already learned that *uni* means "one" and *bi* means "two." You may also know that *tri* means "three." Look in the box for the meanings of several more number prefixes.

Prefix	Meaning	Prefix	Meaning
hemi-	one half	quad-, quart-, quatr-	four
uni-	one	sept-	seven
bi-	two	oct-	eight
tri-	three	dec-	ten

Now read the definitions below. For each definition, find a word that begins with a prefix from the box. (The spelling of the prefix may be slightly changed.) Use a dictionary to search for the word.

Number your paper 1–8 and write the correct word beside each number.

1. a sea animal with eight leg-like tentacles
2. a poem of four lines
3. having two sides
4. half of a globe or sphere
5. to divide into three equal parts
6. the month that was, long ago, the seventh month of the year
7. going in one direction only
8. ten years

D. Expressing Yourself

Choose one of these activities.

1. Most people say the unicorn is an animal of fantasy—that it lives only in stories. Some people say it really exists. Read about the unicorn in an encyclopedia. Then find a story in which a unicorn plays a role. A librarian will be able to help you. Read the story, and prepare a presentation for your class. Begin with a brief report on the legend of the unicorn, using what you learned from the encyclopedia. Then retell the story you have read. Mention what its name means.

2. Write a paragraph using words with all eight prefixes from the box in Part C. You may use words from Parts A, B, and C of this lesson, or find new words in the dictionary. Make the paragraph as silly or serious as you like.

1. The prefix **fore** means **front, before,** or **beforehand. Foresight,** for example, means **seeing beforehand what is going to happen. Foreword** means **the part of a text that** _____ **the main part.**
   (A) comes before   (B) comes after

2. The word that means **to predict or calculate what is about to happen** is _____ .
   (A) forearm   (B) forefinger   (C) forecast

3. The word that means **before midday** is _____ .
   (A) forenoon   (B) foremost   (C) foreknowledge

4. The word that means **to deal with or prevent beforehand** is _____ .
   (A) foremost   (B) forestall   (C) forefoot

5. From the examples we have just studied we can tell that the prefix _____ means **front, before,** or **beforehand.**
   (A) fore   (B) semi   (C) tri

6. The prefix **post** means **after** or **behind.** A **postgraduate** is a student who continues to study after graduation. A **postscript** is a note added to a letter _____ it has been written.
   (A) before   (B) after

7. The word that means **after the war** is _____ .
   (A) postaxial   (B) postdate   (C) postwar

8. The word that means **situated behind** is _____ .
   (A) postpone   (B) posterior   (C) postglacial

9. The word that means **to put off to a later time** is _____ .
   (A) postmortem   (B) postpone   (C) posterity

10. From the examples we have just studied we can tell that the prefix _____ means **after.**
    (A) ante   (B) post   (C) pre

UNIT 14
Prefix Concepts and Practice—in, en

1. The prefix **in** means **in, within, into,** or **toward. Indoors** means **inside a building. Inland** means _____ or **toward the interior.**
   (A) **out of**   (B) **in**

2. The word that means **to breathe in** is _____.
   (A) **inborn**   (B) **inhale**   (C) **inscribe**

3. The word that means **taken in as a part** is _____.
   (A) **included**   (B) **inside**   (C) **incision**

4. The word that means **to enter by force** is _____.
   (A) **incline**   (B) **invade**   (C) **indent**

5. From the examples we have just studied we can tell that the prefix _____ means **in, into, within,** or **toward.**
   (A) **un**   (B) **in**   (C) **ex**

6. The prefix **en** means **in, put into, cover with, make,** or **provide with. Encircle,** for example, means **to make a circle around. Enwrap** means **to cover or wrap. Entitle** means **to** _____ **a title.**
   (A) **provide with**   (B) **take away**

7. The word that means **to make weak** is _____.
   (A) **enfeeble**   (B) **enfold**   (C) **enclose**

8. The word that means **to improve or make wealthy** is _____.
   (A) **engage**   (B) **enrich**   (C) **enlist**

9. The word that means **make greater in quality, value, or importance** is _____.
   (A) **enhance**   (B) **entrench**   (C) **envelop**

10. From the examples we have just studied we can tell that the prefix _____ means **in, put into, cover with, make,** or **provide with.**
    (A) **non**   (B) **en**   (C) **ad**

1. The prefixes **intra** and **intro** mean **within, into, inside of,** or **inwardly.**
Intracellular, for example, means **occurring within a cell or cells.**
Introspection means **looking** _____ **your own thoughts and feelings.**
(A) into   (B) outside of

2. The word that means **within a school** is _____.
(A) intramural   (B) intracardiac   (C) intrapersonal

3. The word that means **within the boundaries of a state** is _____.
(A) intrazonal   (B) intrastate   (C) intramural

4. The word that means **to bring in** is _____.
(A) intravenous   (B) introduce   (C) introvert

5. From the examples we have just studied we can tell that the prefix _____
means **within, into, inside of,** or **inwardly.**
(A) pre   (B) intra   (C) semi

6. The element **mid** means **in the middle of, halfway,** or **among.**
Midafternoon, for example, means **in the middle of the afternoon.**
Midday means **in the middle of the** _____.
(A) day   (B) night

7. The word that means **halfway between the extremes** is _____.
(A) midrib   (B) midpoint   (C) midseason

8. The word that means **the part of the body between the chest and the
abdomen** is _____.
(A) midriff   (B) midmost   (C) midiron

9. The word that means **in the middle of one's lifework** is _____.
(A) midyear   (B) midcareer   (C) midspan

10. From the examples we have just studied we can tell that the element
_____ means **middle, halfway,** or **among.**
(A) fore   (B) mid   (C) pro

UNIT 16
Prefix Concepts and Practice—inter, com

1. The prefix **inter** means **between or with one another. Interstate** means **between states. Interurban** means _____ **cities or towns.**
    (A) over   (B) between

2. The word that means **blend** is _____.
    (A) intermix   (B) international   (C) interoceanic

3. The word that means **between celestial bodies** is _____.
    (A) intertwine   (B) interplanetary   (C) intercollegiate

4. The word that means **the time or space between** is _____.
    (A) interval   (B) intersocial   (C) interweave

5. From the examples we have just studied we can tell that the prefix _____ means **between or with one another.**
    (A) re   (B) inter   (C) mis

6. The prefix **com** means **with** or **together. Compose,** for example, means **make up** or **put together. Compile** means **to gather and put** _____.
    (A) aside   (B) together

7. The word that means **a group of people who live together** is _____.
    (A) community   (B) compress   (C) compile

8. The word that means **to examine in order to find likenesses and differences** is _____.
    (A) common   (B) compare   (C) communicate

9. The word that means **a group of persons or things** is _____.
    (A) compass   (B) company   (C) composition

10. From the examples we have just studied we can tell that the prefix _____ means **with** or **together.**
    (A) com   (B) contra   (C) re

23

1. The prefix **se** means **aside** or **apart.** A **secret,** for example, is **something hidden or kept apart from others. Seclude** means to _____ the company of others.
   (A) **keep together with** (B) **keep apart from**

2. The word that means **to withdraw** or **to go apart** is _____.
   (A) **security**   (B) **selective**   (C) **secede**

3. The word that means **to choose** or **to set apart from the rest** is _____.
   (A) **select**   (B) **secretary**   (C) **secrete**

4. The word that means **one chosen from a group, especially for military service,** is _____.
   (A) **separate**   (B) **selectee**   (C) **secrecy**

5. From the examples we have just studied we can tell that the prefix _____ means **aside** or **apart.**
   (A) **ultra**   (B) **inter**   (C) **se**

6. The prefix **ex** means **out, out of, from,** or **formerly. Exhale,** for example, means **to breathe out.** The **exterior** means the _____ surface.
   (A) **outside**   (B) **inside**

7. The word that means **one taken from a group to show what the others are like** is _____.
   (A) **exchange**   (B) **example**   (C) **exact**

8. The word that means **to send goods out of an area or country** is _____.
   (A) **exhausted**   (B) **execute**   (C) **export**

9. The word that means **a former chief executive** is _____.
   (A) **expand**   (B) **ex-president**   (C) **ex-senator**

10. From the examples we have just studied we can see that the prefix _____ means **out, out of, from,** or **formerly.**
    (A) **tri**   (B) **ex**   (C) **inter**

1. The prefix **trans** means **across, on the other side, through,** or **change into a different condition. Transmigration** means **going from one place or country to another. Transatlantic** means _____ **the Atlantic.**

    (A) **across**   (B) **under**

2. The word that means **to remove blood from the veins of one person and inject it into another person** is _____.

    (A) **translunar**   (B) **transfuse**   (C) **transition**

3. The word that means **to send from one person or place to another** is _____.

    (A) **transmit**   (B) **translation**   (C) **transfusion**

4. The word that means **easy to see through** is _____.

    (A) **transplant**   (B) **transparent**   (C) **transformation**

5. From the examples we have just studied we can tell that the prefix _____ means **across, beyond, on the other side, through,** or **change into a different condition.**

    (A) **trans**   (B) **mal**   (C) **pre**

6. The prefix **per** means **through** or **thoroughly. Permeate,** for example, means **to pass** _____. **Perplex** means **to confuse thoroughly.**

    (A) **through**   (B) **below**

7. The word that means **to puncture** or **to make holes through** is _____.

    (A) **perfume**   (B) **perforate**   (C) **pertinent**

8. The word that means **to cause coffee to pass through filters** is _____.

    (A) **perfect**   (B) **percolate**   (C) **perturb**

9. The word that means **lasting through the whole year** is _____.

    (A) **perfect**   (B) **perennial**   (C) **perturb**

10. From the examples we have just studied we can tell that the prefix _____ means **through** or **thoroughly.**

    (A) **per**   (B) **dis**   (C) **ex**

UNIT 19
Prefix Concepts and Practice—super, ultra

1. The prefix **super** means **above, beyond, over, better than,** or **superior to.** A **supervisor** is one who looks over or who is in charge of other people. A **superhighway** is _____ to an ordinary highway.
    (A) **superior**   (B) **inferior**

2. The word that means **beyond the known forces of nature** is _____.
    (A) **supernatural**   (B) **supercarrier**   (C) **supermarket**

3. The word that means **a nation with great influence** is _____.
    (A) **superfluid**   (B) **superpower**   (C) **superintendent**

4. The word that means **beyond what is needed or desired** is _____.
    (A) **superelastic**   (B) **superpolite**   (C) **superfluous**

5. From the examples we have just studied we can tell that the prefix _____ means **above, beyond, over, better than,** or **superior to.**
    (A) **dis**   (B) **super**   (C) **un**

6. The prefix **ultra** means **beyond** or **to an extreme degree. Ultraviolet,** for example, means **having to do with the spectrum just** _____ **the violet. Ultranational** means **extreme support for a country.**
    (A) **before**   (B) **beyond**

7. The word that means **extremely low in temperature** is _____.
    (A) **ultrafashionable**   (B) **ultracold**   (C) **ultravirus**

8. The word that means **a technique that uses high-frequency sound waves** is _____.
    (A) **ultratropical**   (B) **ultrasound**   (C) **ultramarine**

9. The word that means **beyond the contemporary** is _____.
    (A) **ultramodern**   (B) **ultrascientific**   (C) **ultramicroscopic**

10. From the examples we have just studied we can tell that the prefix _____ means **beyond** or **to an extreme degree.**
    (A) **mis**   (B) **pre**   (C) **ultra**

1. Think about the meaning of **unsafe, uncomfortable, unmask.** The prefix **un** means _____.

   (A) against   (B) to/toward   (C) not/the opposite of

2. Think about the meaning of **semicircle, semiweekly, semiprecious.** The prefix **semi** means _____.

   (A) aside   (B) half/twice   (C) again/back

3. Think about the meaning of **promote, propel, pro-American.** The prefix **pro** means _____.

   (A) after   (B) under/below   (C) forward/in favor of

4. Think about the meaning of **export, exhale, example.** The prefix **ex** means _____.

   (A) between   (B) to/toward   (C) out/from

5. Think about the meaning of **foresight, forearm, foreword.** The prefix **fore** means _____.

   (A) before/front   (B) to/toward   (C) across/beyond

6. Think about the meaning of **inhale, indoors, inland.** The prefix **in** means _____.

   (A) bad/wrong   (B) within/in   (C) out of

7. Think about the meaning of **irrational, irresponsible, irregular.** The prefix **ir** means _____.

   (A) sometimes   (B) not   (C) bad

8. Think about the meaning of **reappear, rearrange, reread.** The prefix **re** means _____.

   (A) again   (B) not   (C) between

9. Think about the meaning of **illegal, illegible, illiterate.** The prefix **il** means _____.

   (A) not   (B) always   (C) move

10. Think about the meaning of **antiaircraft, antisocial, antifreeze.** The prefix **anti** means _____.

    (A) in favor of   (B) to   (C) against/opposite of

1. Think about the meaning of **century, centimeter, centipede.** The prefix **cent** means _____.
   (A) in favor   (B) around   (C) hundred

2. Think about the meaning of **interstate, interplanetary, international.** The prefix **inter** means _____.
   (A) hundred   (B) not/opposite   (C) between

3. Think about the meaning of **midafternoon, midday, midnight.** The prefix **mid** means _____.
   (A) middle   (B) beyond   (C) back

4. Think about the meaning of **bicycle, bisect, biweekly.** The prefix **bi** means _____.
   (A) not   (B) almost   (C) twice/two

5. Think about the meaning of **adhesive, admit, advance.** The prefix **ad** means _____.
   (A) to/toward   (B) three   (C) middle/center

6. Think about the meaning of **contradict, contrary, contraband.** The prefix **contra** means _____.
   (A) in   (B) against/opposite   (C) under/below

7. Think about the meaning of **milligram, millimeter, millisecond.** The prefix **milli** means _____.
   (A) one thousandth of   (B) ten   (C) half

8. Think about the meaning of **monograph, monorail, monotone.** The prefix **mono** means _____.
   (A) hundred   (B) three   (C) one

9. Think about the meaning of **percolate, perforate, perfect.** The prefix **per** means _____.
   (A) not/opposite   (B) through/thoroughly   (C) bad/wrong

10. Think about the meaning of **ultramodern, ultraconfident, ultraloyal.** The prefix **ultra** means _____.
    (A) beyond/to an extreme degree   (B) aside   (C) to/toward

1. Think about the meaning of **absent, abolish, abduct.** The prefix **ab** means

    _____.

    (A) under   **(B) away/from**   **(C) three**

2. Think about the meaning of **oppose, oppression, opposition.** The prefix
   op means _____.

    (A) toward/against   **(B) under**   **(C) up**

3. Think about the meaning of **object, obstacle, obstruction.** The prefix **ob**
   means _____.

    (A) toward/against   **(B) one**   **(C) not/opposite**

4. Think about the meaning of **post-graduate, posterior, postpone.** The
   prefix **post** means _____.

    (A) hundred   **(B) after/behind**   **(C) one**

5. Think about the meaning of **superhighway, supervisor, superman.** The
   prefix **super** means _____.

    (A) above/better than   **(B) partly/twice**   **(C) out of**

6. Think about the meaning of **demolish, descend, detach.** The prefix **de**
   means _____.

    (A) down from/off   **(B) not/no**   **(C) in/within**

7. Think about the meaning of **unicycle, uniform, unit.** The prefix **uni**
   means _____.

    (A) after   **(B) to**   **(C) one**

8. Think about the meaning of **transfer, transatlantic, transplant.** The
   prefix **trans** means _____.

    (A) two   **(B) hundred**   **(C) through/beyond**

9. Think about the meaning of **common, company, companion.** The prefix
   com means _____.

    (A) with/together   **(B) not**   **(C) again/once more**

10. Think about the meaning of **encase, enfold, encircle.** The prefix **en** means

    _____.

    (A) in/cover with   **(B) three**   **(C) not/opposite**

1. Think about the meaning of **triangle, triple, tricycle.** The prefix **tri** means
   _____ .

   (A) half   (B) two   (C) three

2. Think about the meaning of **disappear, distasteful, disloyal.** The prefix **dis** means _____ .

   (A) aside/apart   (B) not/the opposite of   (C) between/middle

3. Think about the meaning of **intramural, intracellular, intraterritorial.** The prefix **intra** means _____ .

   (A) again   (B) two   (C) into/within/ inside of

4. Think about the meaning of **introspection, introduce, introvert.** The prefix **intro** means _____ .

   (A) into/within/ inside of   (B) against   (C) out

5. Think about the meaning of **kilowatt, kilogram, kilometer.** The prefix **kilo** means _____ .

   (A) one thousand   (B) ten   (C) two

6. Think about the meaning of the words **subchief, submerge, subway.** The prefix **sub** can mean **under,** _____ ; or **lower in rank, position, or importance.**

   (A) in   (B) through   (C) below

7. Think about the meaning of the words **subaquatic, subarid, subconscious.** The prefix **sub** can also mean _____ , **somewhat, slightly, again, or further.**

   (A) person   (B) fast   (C) nearly

8. Think about the meaning of the words **overblow, overseer, overbuild.** The prefix **over** can mean **too much, beyond the normal, superior, or** _____ .

   (A) higher in rank   (B) smarter   (C) larger

9. Think about the meaning of the words **overalls, overseas, overhand.** The prefix **over** can also mean **across,** _____ , **or worn as an outer covering.**

   (A) distant   (B) above   (C) without

10. Think about the meaning of **seclude, select, secret.** The prefix **se** means _____ .

    (A) aside/apart   (B) against   (C) not/opposite

1. My sister works as a _____ at the theater.
   - (A) bookstall
   - (B) slingshot
   - (C) candlemaker
   - (D) stagehand
   - (E) password
   - (F) NONE

2. The _____ on the box is very shiny.
   - (A) groundwork
   - (B) giftwrap
   - (C) goddaughter
   - (D) timecard
   - (E) webfoot
   - (F) NONE

3. They bought a car that was in the _____.
   - (A) germfree
   - (B) switchyard
   - (C) showroom
   - (D) halfpenny
   - (E) shinbone
   - (F) NONE

4. It's fun to play in the _____ of the barn.
   - (A) headlock
   - (B) headland
   - (C) headboard
   - (D) hayloft
   - (E) headwind
   - (F) NONE

5. The watch is a very beautiful _____.
   - (A) mantelpiece
   - (B) milepost
   - (C) inkstand
   - (D) time-out
   - (E) timepiece
   - (F) NONE

6. I forgot to put a stamp on the _____.
   - (A) penholder
   - (B) pocketknife
   - (C) postcard
   - (D) barehanded
   - (E) backswing
   - (F) NONE

7. We have to get a plumber to fix the _____.
   - (A) drainpipe
   - (B) gearshift
   - (C) mineshaft
   - (D) earplug
   - (E) drumstick
   - (F) NONE

8. Watch the _____ move all the dirt.
   - (A) blowtorch
   - (B) chessboard
   - (C) bulldozer
   - (D) drillmaster
   - (E) mountaintop
   - (F) NONE

9. Can the _____ make a new set of keys?
   - (A) neckline
   - (B) moneylender
   - (C) paymaster
   - (D) timekeeper
   - (E) locksmith
   - (F) NONE

10. This book is considered a _____.
    - (A) ringmaster
    - (B) tollgate
    - (C) steelyard
    - (D) goalkeeper
    - (E) snakeskin
    - (F) NONE

A compound word is two or more words used together as one word. Sometimes the two words are joined together with no space between them—*bookstore, playground, headache*. Sometimes, they are written with a hyphen—*sister-in-law, hard-boiled, half-moon*. Sometimes the words have a space between them—*price tag, jet stream, roller coaster*. When you are writing, remember that not all compound words are written the same way. Check a dictionary to make sure that you write compound words correctly.

A. Exercising Your Skill

Look around you. Think about what you do during an average day. Compound words are everywhere. We eat, sleep, and drink them (*applesauce, bedtime,* and *teacup*). We work them, study them, play them, and travel them (*songwriter, textbook, football,* and *highway*). They are in our lives "from A to Z."

With little effort you can probably think up twenty or twenty-five compound words. Try it. Just for fun, to show just how widespread compound words are, write the letters of the alphabet on your paper, in a column. Try to write a compound word that begins with each letter of the alphabet, A to Z.

Check a dictionary to make sure your compound words are listed. (For example, *ski jump* is listed in the dictionary as a compound word, but *ski jacket* is not.) Then check each word to see how it is written: Are the two (or more) words joined? Is there a space between them? Is there a hyphen?

B. Expanding Your Skill

How did you do? Some letters are much easier than others, aren't they? Compare your list with your classmates' lists. What words did they find for those letters that you had difficulty with? What new words have you learned? How many of you wrote the same words for some letters? Were there any letters for which you all wrote the same word? for which you all wrote different words?

Spend some time looking through a dictionary. How many new compound words can you find? Add them to your list.

Read this page again. It contains more than twenty compound words. How many of them can you find? Write them on your paper.

C. Exploring Language

Words serve a serious and important purpose for us, but words can also be funny. Many jokes are based on the fact that the same word may have different meanings. This kind of joke is called a pun. That's how compound words can be used to make some very silly puns. Here's an example: What kind of coach works in a theater? A stagecoach! See if you can complete some of these puns by writing a compound word.

1. Q: What kind of card is shaped like a long stick?
   A: A _____ card
2. Q: What kind of fish can be made into jewelry?
   A: A _____ fish
3. Q: What kind of food improves your eyesight?
   A: _____ food
4. Q: What band plays music with a lot of bounce?
   A: A _____ band
5. Q: What can you use to fix a broken tooth?
   A: Tooth _____
6. Q: What kind of boat is always the cheapest?
   A: A _____ boat
7. Q: What do pigs write with?
   A: A pig _____

Now turn this page upside down to check the answers.

Answers: *1. postcard; 2. goldfish; 3. seafood; 4. rubberband; 5. toothpaste; 6. sailboat; 7. pigpen*

D. Expressing Yourself

Choose one of these activities.

1. Find out something about the English alphabet. Where did it come from? Have the letters always been as they are today, or did the alphabet change over time? Write a brief report on the history of the English alphabet. Include a chart showing the English alphabet and two very different alphabets.

2. With several classmates, play a game of "charades" using compound words. Divide into two teams. Each team writes five compound words on individual slips of paper. One player draws a slip from the other team's pile. The player then acts out the compound word for his or her own team to guess.

1. There is a common root in _____.
   (A) audit   (B) specialty
       audio   tentacle

2. There is a common root in _____.
   (A) audition   (B) subtract
       auditor   severance

3. There is a common root in _____.
   (A) audience   (B) salivary
       auditorium   sanctuary

4. So far, all the correct answers have the roots _____.
   (A) sub/sal   (B) aud/audit   (C) scrib/script

5. How many of the following six words have the same root?
   auditory   section   unilateral
   audiometer   sublime   audition
   (A) three   (B) four   (C) five

6. The word that means **capable of being heard** is _____.
   (A) audience   (B) audition   (C) audible

7. The word that means **an instrument that measures how well one hears** is _____.
   (A) audiometer   (B) auditory   (C) audit

8. The word that means **a group of listeners or spectators** is _____.
   (A) audio   (B) audience   (C) auditorium

9. The word that means **referring to both hearing and sight** is _____.
   (A) audiovisual   (B) auditorium   (C) auditor

10. From the examples we have just studied we can tell that the roots **aud** and **audit** mean _____.
    (A) hold   (B) carry   (C) hear

1. There is a common root in _____.
   (A) fluorescent   (B) predict
       generalization   dictionary

2. There is a common root in _____.
   (A) hemisphere   (B) verdict
       impersonal   contradict

3. There is a common root in _____.
   (A) edict   (B) longitude
       dictate   magnificent

4. So far, all the correct answers have the root _____.
   (A) scrib   (B) dict

5. How many of the following six words have the same root?
   prescribe   marvelous   diction
   entertain   edict   dictator
   (A) three   (B) four   (C) five

6. The word that means **the foretelling of a future event** is _____.
   (A) edict   (B) prediction   (C) contradict

7. The word that means **the decision of a jury** is _____.
   (A) verdict   (B) diction   (C) dictator

8. The word that means **the act of speaking words to be written down** is _____.
   (A) predict   (B) contradiction   (C) dictation

9. The word that means **a book that explains the meaning of words** is _____.
   (A) dictionary   (B) verdict   (C) addiction

10. From the examples we have just studied we can tell that the root **dict** means _____.
    (A) tell/say   (B) put/place   (C) take/seize

1. There is a common root in _____.
   (A) special   (B) detection
       specimen   visible

2. There is a common root in _____.
   (A) respect   (B) detention
       inspector   tractor

3. There is a common root in _____.
   (A) conspicuous   (B) invention
       suspicious   retention

4. So far, all the correct answers have the roots _____.
   (A) spec/spic/spect   (B) trac/spect/spec

5. How many of the following six words have the same root?
   prospector   inspect   aspect
   spectacular   vitamin   perspective
   (A) four   (B) five   (C) six

6. A word that means **one who explores or examines a region searching for gold, silver, oil, etc., is _____.**
   (A) prospector   (B) disrespect   (C) spectrum

7. A word that means **something to look at is _____.**
   (A) species   (B) spectacle   (C) respectable

8. A word that means **a person who watches a contest or event is _____.**
   (A) spectator   (B) suspicious   (C) specific

9. A word that means **a close examination is _____.**
   (A) specialty   (B) specific   (C) inspection

10. From the examples we have just studied we can tell that the roots _____ mean **to look at** or **to examine.**
    (A) spec/spic/spect   (B) dic/dict

1. There is a common root in _____.
   (A) admit   (B) revenge
       submit   romance

2. There is a common root in _____.
   (A) signalize   (B) mission
       solemn   dismiss

3. There is a common root in _____.
   (A) permit   (B) stagnant
       commit   successive

4. So far, all the correct answers have the root(s) _____.
   (A) fort   (B) mit/mis(s)   (C) alt/altus

5. How many of the following six words have the same root(s)?
   submit   commit   transmission
   admit   mission   dismiss
   (A) four   (B) five   (C) six

6. The word that means **leave out** is _____.
   (A) transmission   (B) omit   (C) committee

7. The word that means **to send away or allow to leave** is _____.
   (A) commit   (B) dismiss   (C) emit

8. The word that means **a person sent to do special religious work** is _____.
   (A) submit   (B) intermission   (C) missionary

9. The word that means **to allow or let something be done** is _____.
   (A) permit   (B) admit   (C) dismissal

10. From the examples we have just studied we can tell that the roots **mit(t)** and **mis(s)** mean **send** and _____.
    (A) let go   (B) touch   (C) carry

1. There is a common root in _____.
   (A) import   (B) puncture
       reporter   legible

2. There is a common root in _____.
   (A) opportunity   (B) bachelor
       transport   journey

3. There is a common root in _____.
   (A) elevator   (B) portal
       gravel   portfolio

4. So far, all the correct answers have the root _____.
   (A) el   (B) port

5. How many of the following six words have the same root?
   exporter   absorb   foreword
   deport   deportment   import
   (A) three   (B) four   (C) five

6. A word that means **able to be carried** is _____.
   (A) portable   (B) porthole   (C) reportable

7. A word that means **an entrance** is _____.
   (A) importance   (B) port   (C) reportorial

8. A word that means **one who carries luggage** is _____.
   (A) comport   (B) sport   (C) porter

9. A word that means **to send or carry out of the country** is _____.
   (A) export   (B) sportsman   (C) portly

10. From the examples we have just studied we can tell that the root _____
    means **carry, entrance,** or **harbor.**
    (A) port   (B) scribe

1. There is a common root in _____.
   (A) preview   (B) depose
       pronounce   impose

2. There is a common root in _____.
   (A) substantial   (B) opponent
       survey   component

3. There is a common root in _____.
   (A) theoretical   (B) opposite
       tradition   position

4. So far, all the correct answers have the root(s) _____.
   (A) pos/pon   (B) reg   (C) fac

5. How many of the following six words have the same root?
   magistrate   advertise   position
   composer   superimpose   opposite
   (A) four   (B) five   (C) six

6. The word that means **to put parts together** is _____.
   (A) compose   (B) impose   (C) transposition

7. The word that means **face to face** or **placed against** is _____.
   (A) opposite   (B) depose   (C) composer

8. The word that means **to put off until a later date** is _____.
   (A) position   (B) postpone   (C) imposition

9. The word that means **to change the position or order of** is _____.
   (A) superimpose   (B) transpose   (C) depository

10. From the examples we have just studied we can tell that the roots **pos** and **pon** mean _____.
    (A) put/place   (B) again/repeat   (C) tell/hear

1. There is a common root in _____.
    (A) manual   (B) tenant
        manuscript   stylist

2. There is a common root in _____.
    (A) manacle   (B) mackinaw
        emancipate   magical

3. There is a common root in _____.
    (A) indistinct   (B) manipulation
        indignant   mandate

4. So far, all the correct answers have the root _____.
    (A) script   (B) man   (C) spect

5. How many of the following six words have the same root?
    manufacture   manacle   manicure
    empire   mundane   expensive
    (A) three   (B) four   (C) five

6. The word that means **to trim, clean, and polish the fingernails** is _____.
    (A) manicure   (B) manipulate   (C) mandate

7. The word that means **handcuffs** is _____.
    (A) manacles   (B) manufacture   (C) manage

8. The word that means **by hand** is _____.
    (A) manually   (B) emancipate   (C) mannerly

9. The word that means **a book or paper written by hand or on a typewriter** is _____.
    (A) manicurist   (B) manufacturing   (C) manuscript

10. From the examples we have just studied we can tell that the root **man** means _____.
    (A) hand   (B) foot   (C) hear

UNIT 32
Root Concepts and Practice—scrib(e), script

1. There is a common root in _____.
    (A) manuscript   (B) recollection
        inscription   perspiration

2. There is a common root in _____.
    (A) spontaneous   (B) inscribe
        stereoscope   subscribe

3. There is a common root in _____.
    (A) territory   (B) scribble
        theatrical   proscribe

4. So far, all the correct answers have the root(s) _____.
    (A) cred/spect   (B) dect   (C) script/scrib(e)

5. How many of the following six words have the same root?
    prescript   postscript   inscription
    manuscript   scripture   subscription
    (A) four   (B) five   (C) six

6. The word that means **tell what something is like** is _____.
    (A) scribble   (B) describe   (C) transcribe

7. The word that means **the written addition that follows a book or article**
    is _____.
    (A) inscribe   (B) postscript   (C) subscription

8. The word that means **to write carelessly and hastily** is _____.
    (A) subscribe   (B) scribble   (C) prescription

9. The word that means **a written direction for preparing and using
    medicine** is _____.
    (A) scripture   (B) prescription   (C) manuscript

10. From the examples we have just studied we can tell that the roots **scribe**
    and **script** mean _____.
    (A) hold   (B) write   (C) break

1. There is a common root in _____.
   (A) accessible   (B) incapable
        accident   receive

2. There is a common root in _____.
   (A) capture   (B) disadvantage
        receipt   entangle

3. There is a common root in _____.
   (A) receptacle   (B) inability
        incipient   investigate

4. So far, all the correct answers have the root(s) _____.
   (A) cap/cip/cept/   (B) cept/scrib/reg   (C) cap/ten/polio
   ceive/ceipt

5. How many of the following six words have the same root?
   exceptional   acceptance   regulation
   receptionist   misconception   repetition
   (A) four   (B) five   (C) three

6. The word that means **having skill and ability** is _____.
   (A) conceited   (B) capable   (C) intercept

7. The word that means **remarkable or unusual** is _____.
   (A) exceptional   (B) receive   (C) concept

8. The word that means **to seize by force** is _____.
   (A) acceptance   (B) incapable   (C) capture

9. The word that means **to take** or **agree to** is _____.
   (A) deceptive   (B) accept   (C) inception

10. From the examples we have just studied we can tell that the roots **cap, cip, cept, ceive,** and **ceipt** mean _____.
    (A) picture   (B) take   (C) time

UNIT 34
Root Concepts and Practice—fact

1. There is a common root in _____.
   - (A) example
     - consonant
   - (B) factory
     - manufacture

2. There is a common root in _____.
   - (A) perfect
     - defect
   - (B) intricate
     - limitation

3. There is a common root in _____.
   - (A) difficult
     - efficient
   - (B) luminous
     - miniature

4. So far, all the correct answers have the root(s) _____.
   - (A) fect/fact/fic
   - (B) graph/gram
   - (C) cap/capt/cept

5. How many of the following six words have the same root(s)?
   - factory
   - defect
   - manufacture
   - difficult
   - perfect
   - introduce
   - (A) four
   - (B) five
   - (C) six

6. The word that means **a story that is made up** is _____.
   - (A) fiction
   - (B) fact
   - (C) difficult

7. The word that means **something that is made similar to something else** is _____.
   - (A) fashion
   - (B) facsimile
   - (C) fortification

8. The word that means **made with a fault or weakness** is _____.
   - (A) confection
   - (B) perfect
   - (C) defective

9. The word that means **a building where things are made or manufactured** is _____.
   - (A) factory
   - (B) efficient
   - (C) faction

10. From the examples we have just studied we can tell that the roots **fac, fact,** and **fect** mean **do,** _____, or **cause.**
    - (A) make
    - (B) carry
    - (C) say

1. Think of the meaning of the words **audience, audiovisual, audition.** The roots **aud** and **audit** mean _____.
   (A) see   (B) hear   (C) hurt

2. Think of the meaning of the words **inspector, spectator, expect.** The root **spec** means _____.
   (A) look/examine   (B) entire   (C) part

3. Think of the meaning of the words **porter, portable, export.** The root **port** means _____.
   (A) difficult   (B) write   (C) carry/harbor

4. Think of the meaning of the words **mission, submit, dismiss.** The roots **mit** and **mis** mean _____.
   (A) heat/warmth   (B) send/let go   (C) dead

5. Think of the meaning of the words **dictate, verdict, contradict.** The root **dict** means _____.
   (A) find   (B) say/tell   (C) angle

6. Think of the meaning of the words **compose, position, deposit.** The roots **pos** and **pon** mean _____.
   (A) put/place   (B) make/also   (C) go back/return

7. Think of the meaning of the words **factory, manufacture, fiction.** The roots **fact, fect,** and **fic** mean _____.
   (A) hand   (B) make/cause   (C) look/examine

8. Think of the meaning of the words **accept, capture, receive.** The roots **capt, cip, cept, ceive,** and **ceipt** mean _____.
   (A) send   (B) sign   (C) take

9. Think of the meaning of the words **manicure, manually, manipulate.** The roots **man** and **manu** mean _____.
   (A) hand   (B) foot   (C) head

10. Think of the meaning of the words **manuscript, describe, subscribe.** The roots **scrib** and **script** mean _____.
    (A) write   (B) speak   (C) act

UNIT 36
Suffix Concepts and Practice

1. Of all the suffixes that mean **one who** and **that which,** the most common is _____. A **singer,** for example, is one who sings. A **painter** is one who paints.
   (A) er   (B) ant   (C) tion

2. The word that means **one who sells foodstuffs and household supplies** is _____.
   (A) grocer   (B) reader   (C) islander

3. Another suffix that means **one who** and **that which** is _____. A **survivor** is one who survives. An **accelerator** is that which accelerates or increases the speed.
   (A) less   (B) or   (C) en

4. Choose a word that means **one who leads, guides, or directs.**
   (A) conductor   (B) janitor   (C) actor

5. A suffix with the same meaning is _____. A **taxidermist** is one who is engaged in taxidermy. An **optometrist** is one who is engaged in optometry.
   (A) taxi   (B) ist   (C) ness

6. Choose the word that means **one who knows about plant life.**
   (A) botanist   (B) machinist   (C) idealist

7. Two other suffixes that mean **one who** and **that which** are _____ and _____. An **American** is one who lives in America. A **librarian** is one who works in a library.
   (A) full/less   (B) an/ian   (C) ic/ary

8. Choose the word that means **one who cares for the sick.**
   (A) physician   (B) mortician   (C) electrician

9. Two more suffixes with the same meaning are _____ and _____. A **cashier** is one who pays out and receives cash. An **auctioneer** is one who conducts auctions.
   (A) ity/ty   (B) tial/tral   (C) ier/eer

10. Choose the word that means **one who makes an excessive amount of money.**
    (A) profiteer   (B) privateer   (C) charioteer

1. The suffix _____ means **one who,** but it is applied to females. A **lioness** is a female lion. A **goddess** is a female god.
   (A) er   (B) ess   (C) ist

2. Choose the word that means **one who entertains guests.**
   (A) hostess   (B) heiress   (C) actress

3. The suffix _____ means **one who.** An **appointee** is one who is appointed. An **absentee** is one who isn't present.
   (A) ly   (B) ee   (C) less

4. Choose the word that means **the one to whom a gift is made.**
   (A) donee   (B) absentee   (C) draftee

5. _____ is a suffix with the same meaning. One who creates puns is a **punster.** One who sings songs is a **songster.**
   (A) Ster   (B) Ment   (C) Ness

6. Choose the word that means **one who plays tricks.**
   (A) teamster   (B) prankster   (C) monster

7. Other suffixes with the same meaning are _____ and _____. A **servant** is one who serves. A **superintendent** is one who supervises or directs.
   (A) kin/ic   (B) ent/ant   (C) able/ible

8. Choose the word that means **one who aids or helps.**
   (A) dependent   (B) assistant   (C) president

9. Two more suffixes with the same meaning are _____ and _____. A **coward,** for example, is one who lacks courage. A **braggart** is one who brags and boasts.
   (A) et/eth   (B) int/ent   (C) ard/art

10. Choose a word that means **one who lags behind.**
    (A) laggard   (B) coward   (C) braggart

UNIT 38
Suffix Concepts and Practice

1. **Strengthen** means to **make or become stronger. Woolen** means **made of wool.** In such words the suffix _____ means **to make** or **to become.**
   (A) en
   (B) th
   (C) ist

2. Choose the word that means **to make more broad.**
   (A) soften
   (B) widen
   (C) sicken

3. **Mobilize** means **to make or become mobile. Visualize** means **to make visual.** In such words the suffix _____ means **to make** or **to become.**
   (A) en
   (B) ize
   (C) ent

4. Choose the word that means **to make orderly.**
   (A) civilize
   (B) systemize
   (C) legalize

5. **Beautify** means **to make or become beautiful. Liquefy** means **to make or become liquid.** The suffix _____ means **to make** or **to become.**
   (A) less
   (B) fy
   (C) ful

6. Choose the word that means **to make easy.**
   (A) simplify
   (B) solidify
   (C) citify

7. **Cheerfully** means **in the manner of being cheerful. Ghostly** means **like a ghost.** The suffix _____ means **in the manner of** or **like.**
   (A) less
   (B) ly
   (C) ment

8. Choose the word that means **slowly** or **not all at once.**
   (A) hastily
   (B) gradually
   (C) partly

9. **Crosswise** means **in the position or direction of a cross. Crabwise** means **in the manner of a crab.** The suffix _____ means **in the manner, position, direction,** or **reference.**
   (A) ate
   (B) tion
   (C) wise

10. Choose the word that means **in the same manner.**
    (A) likewise
    (B) nowise
    (C) slantwise

A word root is a word part that can form the base of many words. It is the main part of a word to which one or more prefixes and suffixes may be added. Like prefixes and suffixes, word roots have meanings of their own. Most word roots come from Latin and Greek. Look for a familiar word root when you see an unfamiliar word. If you know the meaning of the root, you just may be able to figure out the meaning of the word.

A. Exercising Your Skill

They say "seeing is believing"—seeing something is proof that it exists, that it is real. Sometimes hearing and saying are proof, too. Our eyes and ears and mouths are all used for communication, and we would have a hard time knowing anything if we did not communicate.

Look at the word roots in the box. Which ones have something to do with seeing, saying, hearing, or writing? Make a larger copy of the communication word web below. Write the correct root(s) under each heading. Then write as many words as you can think of that contain the root(s).

aud	cap	dict	spec/spic/spect	man
mit	port	pos/pon	scrib(e)/script	

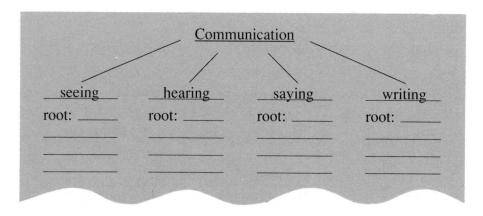

B. Expanding Your Skill

Talk about your communicating words with your classmates. Do you know the meaning of all the words you wrote? Does each relate to communication? How? Are there other words you can add to your word web? Look in a dictionary or other word book to find new words containing these roots.

C. Exploring Language

People who make movies record sights and sounds for safekeeping. Technology allows us to save sights and sounds today, too. We can use photographs and tape recorders or video cameras. Just as a movie director has a story map to know what comes next, you will need a story map to plan which sights and sounds you want to save.

First choose a part of a day or a special event. Make a list of things you will photograph. Then make a list of what you might hear and will want to record. Include the smallest details. They make the memories clear.

Now use your lists to write a paragraph about the sights and sounds you will put away for safekeeping in your memory. Try to include some of the word roots from this lesson.

D. Expressing Yourself

Choose one of these activities.

1. A prediction is something that someone says will happen. What do you think will happen next week, next month, next year, in two or three or five years? What will happen in science? What will happen in the way we are taught in school? What will happen in our town or city? Write down your predictions and put them in a safe place. Make one prediction about your country or state, one prediction about your town or city, and one prediction about yourself in the next five years. Take them out and read them at some time in the future to see how well you did.

2. Magazines are a popular form of communication in our society. Most magazines have a theme, such as sailing, cooking, fashion, computers, or science fiction. Choose a topic—any topic especially interesting to you—as a theme for a magazine. Imagine that you are planning the first issue. First make up a title for the magazine. Then decide what reports, stories, and special features this issue will include. List all of your articles in a table of contents. Make up titles that would catch a reader's interest but that also give a clear idea of what the articles are about. Now think about advertisements. Usually, a business wants to advertise in a magazine whose theme is somehow related to its product. What products would be suitable to advertise in your magazine? Try to list ten.

1. **Changeable** means **able to be changed. Solvable** means **capable of being solved.** The suffix _____ means **capable of.**
   (A) ful   (B) able   (C) less

2. Choose a word that means **able to be marketed.**
   (A) salable   (B) perishable   (C) collectible

3. **Glorious** means **having much glory. Poisonous** means **full of poison.** The suffix _____ means **full of** or **having a tendency to.**
   (A) ous   (B) ent   (C) able

4. Choose a word that means **having much danger.**
   (A) thunderous   (B) perilous   (C) joyous

5. **Boyish** means **like a boy. Thievish** means **tending or inclined to steal.** The suffix _____ means **like that of** or **having a tendency to.**
   (A) ent   (B) ful   (C) ish

6. Choose a word that means **like a female.**
   (A) childish   (B) girlish   (C) sweetish

7. **Active** means **tending to act. Corrective** means **having a tendency to correct.** The suffix _____ means **having a tendency to.**
   (A) less   (B) er   (C) ive

8. Choose a word that means **having a tendency to ruin or spoil.**
   (A) destructive   (B) creative   (C) massive

9. **Harmless** means **without harm. Motherless** means **without a mother.** The suffix _____ means **devoid of** or **without.**
   (A) less   (B) ful   (C) ment

10. Choose a word that means **without fault.**
    (A) blameless   (B) toothless   (C) iceless

1. **Musical** means **pertaining to music. Betrayal** means **the act of betraying.** The suffix _____ means **pertaining to** or **the act of.**
   (A) ful   (B) al   (C) less

2. Choose the word that means **the act of declaring something not true.**
   (A) refusal   (B) denial   (C) portrayal

3. **Detection** means **the act of detecting. Completion** means **the state of being completed.** The suffix _____ means **the act of** or **the state of being.**
   (A) kin   (B) tion   (C) ster

4. Choose the word that means **the act of making or causing to be.**
   (A) temptation   (B) relation   (C) creation

5. **Management** means **the act or state of managing. Astonishment** means **the state of being astonished.** The suffix _____ means **the act of** or **the state of being.**
   (A) ology   (B) ment   (C) er

6. Choose the word that means **the act or state of growth.**
   (A) entertainment   (B) development   (C) government

7. **Darkness** means **the state or quality of being dark. Goodness** means **the state or quality of being good.** The suffix _____ means **the state or quality of being.**
   (A) ness   (B) ee   (C) ist

8. Choose the word that means **the state or quality of not being fresh.**
   (A) kindness   (B) sadness   (C) staleness

9. **Seizure** means **the act or process of seizing. Portraiture** means **the act or process of painting a portrait.** The suffix _____ means **the act or process of.**
   (A) ure   (B) ly   (C) ard

10. Choose the word that means **the act or state of being shown or in plain sight.**
    (A) exposure   (B) pressure   (C) rupture

UNIT 41
Suffix Concepts and Practice

1. A **lambkin** is a little lamb. A **manikin** is a very small man. The suffix _____ means **little.**
   (A) **tion**   (B) **kin**   (C) **ent**

2. Choose the word that means **a little piece of cloth.**
   (A) **napkin**   (B) **catkin**   (C) **ramekin**

3. A **droplet** is a little drop. An **anklet** is a band or ornament worn around the ankle. The suffix _____ means **little** or **a band.**
   (A) **let**   (B) **ment**   (C) **ness**

4. Choose the word that means **a little wave.**
   (A) **bracelet**   (B) **wristlet**   (C) **wavelet**

5. A **particle** is a small part. The suffix _____ means **small.**
   (A) **ent**   (B) **cle**   (C) **est**

6. Choose the word that means **a small space.**
   (A) **pinnacle**   (B) **cubicle**   (C) **particle**

7. A **kitchenette** is a small kitchen. An **usherette** is a female usher. The suffix _____ means **small** or **feminine.**
   (A) **ette**   (B) **ing**   (C) **art**

8. Choose the word that means **a small figurine or model.**
   (A) **statuette**   (B) **collarette**   (C) **farmerette**

9. **Annie** means **little Ann** or **darling Ann. Dearie** means **one who is small or much loved.** The suffix _____ means **small** or **beloved.**
   (A) **ie**   (B) **est**   (C) **ent**

10. Choose the word that means **a much loved boy.**
    (A) **lassie**   (B) **dearie**   (C) **laddie**

UNIT 42
Suffix Concepts and Practice

1. **Bronchitis** is an inflammation of the bronchial tubes. **Peritonitis** is an inflammation of the peritoneum. The suffix _____ means **an inflammation of.**
   (A) ess   (B) itis   (C) ure

2. Choose the word that means **an inflammation of the appendix.**
   (A) peritonitis   (B) gastritis   (C) appendicitis

3. An **anagram** is a word or phrase formed from another by transposing the letters. An **autograph** is one's name written in one's own handwriting. The elements _____ mean **letter** or **writing.**
   (A) dem/demo   (B) gram/graph   (C) aut/auto

4. Choose the word that means **the story of someone's life.**
   (A) autograph   (B) phonograph   (C) biography

5. **Homicide** means murder. **Insecticide** is something used to kill insects. The element _____ means **killing** or **able to kill.**
   (A) cide   (B) ness   (C) ent

6. Choose the word that means **killing the king.**
   (A) pesticide   (B) germicide   (C) regicide

7. A **thermometer** measures temperature. An **anemometer** measures wind speed. The element _____ means **measure.**
   (A) meter   (B) ee   (C) let

8. Choose the word that means **an instrument that measures air pressure.**
   (A) barometer   (B) altimeter   (C) speedometer

9. **Zoology** is the study or science of animal life. **Ornithology** is the study or science of birds. The element _____ means **the study or science of.**
   (A) ity   (B) ology   (C) eer

10. Choose the word that means **the study or science of the human mind.**
    (A) psychology   (B) biology   (C) astrology

1. **Terrorism** is a state of terror. **Criticism** is the act or practice of criticizing. The suffix _____ means **the state or act of.**
   (A) **art**   (B) **ism**   (C) **fy**

2. Choose the word that means **the state or act of hypnotizing.**
   (A) **nationalism**   (B) **hypnotism**   (C) **heroism**

3. **Earldom** is the rank of being an earl. **Freedom** is the state or condition of being free. The suffix _____ means **state of** or **rank of.**
   (A) **or**   (B) **dom**   (C) **ist**

4. Choose the word that means **those having a position or rank of authority.**
   (A) **heathendom**   (B) **freedom**   (C) **officialdom**

5. **Childhood** means **the state of being a child. Knighthood** means **belonging to a group of knights.** The suffix _____ means **the state of being or belonging to a class or group.**
   (A) **less**   (B) **hood**   (C) **ize**

6. Choose the word that means **a state of maturity.**
   (A) **adulthood**   (B) **knighthood**   (C) **livelihood**

7. **Governorship** means **the state or rank of being governor. Horseman-ship** means **the art or skill of handling a horse.** The suffix _____ means **the state, rank, or skill of.**
   (A) **ful**   (B) **er**   (C) **ship**

8. Choose the word that means **the skill of shooting accurately.**
   (A) **marksmanship**   (B) **friendship**   (C) **kinship**

9. **Avoidance** is the act of avoiding. **Dependence** is the state of being dependent. The suffixes _____ and _____ mean **the act or state of.**
   (A) **er/or**   (B) **ance/ence**   (C) **ard/art**

10. Choose the word that means **the state of being certain.**
    (A) **confidence**   (B) **independence**   (C) **annoyance**

UNIT 44
Suffix Concepts and Practice

1. **Atmospheric** means **pertaining to atmosphere. Angelic** means **resembling an angel.** The suffix _____ means **pertaining to** or **resembling.**
   (A) ist   (B) ic   (C) or

2. The word that means **resembling a second year high school or college student** is _____.
   (A) heroic   (B) sophomoric   (C) phonographic

3. The suffix _____ means **pertaining to. Honorary,** for example, pertains to honor. **Legendary** pertains to legends.
   (A) is   (B) ary   (C) eer

4. The word that means **pertaining to the armed forces** is _____.
   (A) secondary   (B) military   (C) salutary

5. **Skillful** means **having skill. Thoughtful** means **tending to thought.** The suffix _____ means **having, full of,** or **tending to.**
   (A) ful   (B) tion   (C) less

6. The word that means **having a tendency to sadness** is _____.
   (A) careful   (B) helpful   (C) mournful

7. The suffix _____ means **to become, have,** or **like. Maturate,** for example, means **to become mature. Compassionate** means **having compassion.**
   (A) ier   (B) ent   (C) ate

8. The word that means **having luck** is _____.
   (A) affectionate   (B) fortunate   (C) desolate

9. The suffix _____ means **pertaining to,** or **tending to. Singular,** for example, pertains to single. **Polar** pertains to the Earth's poles.
   (A) let   (B) ar   (C) less

10. The word that means **normal** or **according to schedule** is _____.
    (A) titular   (B) regular   (C) circular

1. The suffix _____ means **full of, having, somewhat, tending to,** or **state of. Cloudy** means **full of clouds. Lumpy** means **having lumps. Jealousy** is **the state of being jealous.**
   (A) or   (B) y   (C) hood

2. The word that means **the state of being the winner** is _____.
   (A) minority   (B) victory   (C) slavery

3. The suffix _____ means **the state or condition of. The state of being necessary** is **necessity. The condition of motherhood** is **maternity.**
   (A) ice   (B) ity   (C) ien

4. The word that means **a condition of higher quality** is _____.
   (A) superiority   (B) inferiority   (C) brutality

5. The suffix _____ means **the condition or act of. Cowardice** means **the state of being a coward.**
   (A) ish   (B) ice   (C) less

6. The word that means **the act or condition of helping someone** is _____.
   (A) malice   (B) notice   (C) service

7. The suffix _____ means **the state of. Marriage,** for example, means **the state of being married.**
   (A) ate   (B) age   (C) yer

8. The word that means **the state of being carried or transported** is _____.
   (A) leafage   (B) haulage   (C) dosage

9. The suffix _____ means **pertaining to** or **a place. Advisory** means **pertaining to advice. Laboratory** means **a place to conduct science experiments.**
   (A) ness   (B) ship   (C) ory

10. The word that means **a place for housing students** is _____.
    (A) depository   (B) dormitory   (C) observatory

1. Think about the meaning of **conductor, janitor, aviator.** The suffix **or** means _____.

   (A) full   (B) the state of   (C) one who

2. Think about the meaning of **qualify, beautify, satisfy.** The suffix **fy** means _____.

   (A) without   (B) little   (C) make/become

3. Think about the meaning of particle, pinnacle, cubicle. The suffix **cle** means _____.

   (A) little   (B) state of   (C) one who

4. Think about the meaning of **maturate, compassionate, affectionate.** The suffix **ate** means _____.

   (A) without   (B) little   (C) having/tending to

5. Think about the meaning of **bronchitis, appendicitis, peritonitis.** The suffix **itis** means _____.

   (A) inflammation of   (B) state of   (C) little

6. Think about the meaning of **cloudy, victory, jealousy.** The suffix **y** means _____.

   (A) full of/state of   (B) little   (C) without

7. Think about the meaning of **pesticide, homicide, germicide.** The suffix **cide** means _____.

   (A) make/become   (B) kill/able to kill   (C) full of

8. Think about the meaning of **absentee, draftee, employee.** The suffix **ee** means _____.

   (A) one who   (B) the state of   (C) without

9. Think about the meaning of **denial, classical, natural.** The suffix **al** means _____.

   (A) pertaining to/   (B) one who   (C) without
        act of

10. Think about the meaning of **doubtless, harmless, careless.** The suffix **less** means _____.

   (A) ful   (B) without   (C) one who

1. Think about the meaning of **exposure, pressure, failure.** The suffix **ure** means _____.

   (A) little   (B) one who   (C) state of/act of

2. Think about the meaning of **childhood, falsehood, brotherhood.** The suffix **hood** means _____.

   (A) state of/   (B) one who   (C) without
        belonging to

3. Think about the meaning of **lengthwise, clockwise, bookwise.** The suffix **wise** means _____.

   (A) manner/direction   (B) little   (C) without

4. Think about the meaning of **servant, superintendent, president.** The suffixes **ant** and **ent** mean _____.

   (A) little   (B) the state of   (C) one who

5. Think about the meaning of **service, cowardice, notice.** The suffix **ice** means _____.

   (A) state of/act of   (B) little   (C) without

6. Think about the meaning of **manikin, lambkin, napkin.** The suffix **kin** means _____.

   (A) full of   (B) little   (C) without

7. Think about the meaning of **atmospheric, angelic, heroic.** The suffix **ic** means _____.

   (A) little   (B) pertaining to   (C) without

8. Think about the meaning of **rocketeer, engineer, cashier.** The suffixes **eer** and **ier** mean _____.

   (A) one who   (B) without   (C) to make

9. Think about the meaning of **joyous, poisonous, thunderous.** The suffix **ous** means _____.

   (A) without   (B) one who   (C) full of

10. Think about the meaning of **terrorism, criticism, heroism.** The suffix **ism** means _____.

    (A) state of/act of   (B) little   (C) one who

1. Think about the meaning of **biology, zoology, ecology.** The suffix **ology** means _____.

   (A) without   (B) little   (C) study of

2. Think about the meaning of **soften, lengthen, sicken.** The suffix **en** means _____.

   (A) make/become   (B) without   (C) one who

3. Think about the meaning of **singular, popular, polar.** The suffix **ar** means _____.

   (A) pertaining to   (B) without   (C) little

4. Think about the meaning of **lioness, hostess, poetess.** The suffix **ess** means _____.

   (A) to make   (B) without   (C) female

5. Think about the meaning of **detection, completion, relation.** The suffix **tion** means _____.

   (A) state of/act of   (B) little   (C) one who

6. Think about the meaning of **Annie, birdie, kitty.** The suffixes **ie** and **y** mean _____.

   (A) full of   (B) small/much loved   (C) without

7. Think about the meaning of **dormitory, depository, advisory.** The suffix **ory** means _____.

   (A) without   (B) pertaining to/   (C) little
                                         place where

8. Think about the meaning of **reader, grocer, rider.** The suffix **er** means _____.

   (A) the act of   (B) one who   (C) little

9. Think about the meaning of **friendship, kingship, clerkship.** The suffix **ship** means _____.

   (A) without   (B) state of being   (C) one who

10. Think about the meaning of **whitish, childish, clownish.** The suffix **ish** means _____.

    (A) tending/inclined to   (B) one who   (C) little

1. Think about the meaning of **autograph, telegram, paragraph.** The elements **graph** and **gram** mean _____.

    (A) state of   (B) without   (C) letter/writing

2. Think about the meaning of **active, creative, corrective.** The suffix **ive** means _____.

    (A) tending to   (B) little   (C) without

3. Think about the meaning of **honorary, customary, military.** The suffix **ary** means _____.

    (A) without   (B) pertaining to   (C) little

4. Think about the meaning of **idealist, machinist, zoologist.** The suffix **ist** means _____.

    (A) without   (B) the state of   (C) one who

5. Think about the meaning of **droplet, eyelet, booklet.** The suffix **let** means _____.

    (A) full of   (B) state of   (C) little

6. Think about the meaning of **confidence, assistance, resistance.** The suffixes **ance** and **ence** mean _____.

    (A) little   (B) state of/act of   (C) without

7. Think about the meaning of **development, astonishment, government.** The suffix **ment** means _____.

    (A) little   (B) without   (C) state of/act of

8. Think about the meaning of **songster, gangster, prankster.** The suffix **ster** means _____.

    (A) one who   (B) the state of   (C) to make

9. Think about the meaning of **marriage, leafage, parentage.** The suffix **age** means _____.

    (A) little   (B) state of   (C) without

10. Think about the meaning of **partly, brotherly, quickly.** The suffix **ly** means _____.

    (A) manner of   (B) little   (C) without

1. Think about the meaning of **necessity, superiority, rapidity.** The suffix
   ity means _____.
   (A) state of   **(B) little**   **(C) without**

2. Think about the meaning of **electrician, veteran, Canadian.** The suffixes
   ian and **an** mean _____.
   (A) to make   **(B) one who**   **(C) large**

3. Think about the meaning of **statuette, kitchenette, dinette.** The suffix
   ette means _____.
   (A) one who   **(B) little**   **(C) without**

4. Think about the meaning of **thermometer, anemometer, speedometer.**
   The element **meter** means _____.
   (A) without   **(B) measure**   **(C) make/become**

5. Think about the meaning of **likable, eatable, changeable.** The suffixes
   able and **ible** mean _____.
   (A) without   **(B) able/capable**   **(C) one who**

6. Think about the meaning of **wisdom, kingdom, boredom.** The suffix **dom**
   means _____.
   (A) state of/rank of   **(B) without**   **(C) one who**

7. Think about the meaning of **legalize, sterilize, civilize.** The suffix **ize**
   means _____.
   (A) make/become   **(B) little**   **(C) one who**

8. Think about the meaning of **coward, laggard, braggart.** The suffixes **art**
   and **ard** mean _____.
   (A) one who   **(B) without**   **(C) little**

9. Think about the meaning of **skillful, thankful, beautiful.** The suffix **ful**
   means _____.
   (A) full of/tending to   **(B) without**   **(C) little**

10. Think about the meaning of **wilderness, goodness, sickness.** The suffix
    ness means _____.
    (A) one who   **(B) state of/quality of**   **(C) without**

Suffixes are word parts that are added at the end of a root word. Suffixes have meanings of their own and change the meaning of the words they are attached to. They cannot act as words by themselves. Many suffixes have the same or similar meanings. The suffixes *y, ity, age, hood, ice, ism, ship, ance, ence, tion, ment, dom,* and *ness,* for instance, can all mean "state of." For example, *wisdom* means "the state of being wise."

A. Exercising Your Skill

"How are you?" is perhaps the most common greeting we have. Usually, when asked, we simply say "Fine" or "Pretty well" or "Not bad." If a good friend asks the question, we might give a few details: happy because we got a good grade on a test, worried because of a test coming up. There are many words to describe how we feel.

Look at the suffixes below. Then look at the words in the box. Each word can be used to describe the way someone is feeling. On your paper, combine each word in the box with one of the suffixes to write a word that names the state or condition of having that feeling. For example, the state of being happy is happiness. Then think about other words that can be used to describe how you feel. Do they contain these suffixes? If they do, add them to the lists. If they do not, write them in another list. Check all of your words in a dictionary to make sure you have spelled them correctly.

ness	ment	ance/ence	ity
_____	_____	_____	_____
_____	_____	_____	_____
_____	_____	_____	_____
_____	_____	_____	_____

happy	sad	impatient	nervous	confident
sincere	excited	tolerant	anxious	merry

B. Expanding Your Skill

How did you do? Compare your lists with your classmates' lists. Can you add any new words to your lists? How might you find other words to describe how you feel?

C. Exploring Language

You are afraid. You are anxious. You want to write about your feelings, but what can you say to describe how you feel? You brainstorm for a few minutes and add *frightened*, *nervous*, and *worried* to your list. That gives you a good place to start. It also gives you an idea of some questions to ask yourself.

What am I worried about?
What is it here that is frightening? A sound? Something I saw?
    Something I heard?
What is making me nervous?
With some questions like these in hand, starting to write is not so hard.

Think about times you were very sad, angry, excited, or happy. Choose one to write about. What words with suffixes can you use to describe how you felt? What questions can you ask? Write a paragraph about the experience you have chosen. Tell more about how you felt than about what happened.

D. Expressing Yourself

Choose one of these activities.

1. Actors have to be able to turn their feelings off and on. When they are rehearsing or performing, they must be prepared to act out emotions of happiness, anger, jealousy, fear—whatever their role calls for. They may have to express different emotions from one minute to the next. How quickly can you change the feeling you are expressing? With a classmate, hold an actor's workshop. Take turns being the actor and the director. The director names an emotion for the actor to express. While the actor is still expressing it, the director cuts in suddenly with another emotion. After the director has named three or four emotions, the actor and director switch roles.

2. Popular songs usually express one main feeling. Some of the most common feelings we hear in songs are happiness, excitement, jealousy, and loneliness—but there are many more. Find a radio station that plays popular songs, and listen for four or more different feelings. Write down the names of the songs and the feelings they express.

CONCEPTS DEVELOPED